Jamuna

This book belongs to

____

Written by Stephen Barnett
Illustrated by Rosie Brooks

Contents

About this book

Two wonderful stories to encourage children to get into the habit of reading. The new words that readers will come across here and the illustrations that accompany the stories will help children to sharpen their awareness of the world around them.

The seagull that came to stay

It was summer holidays. We were outside playing in the garden when we first noticed the bird.

'What bird is that?' my sister Selina asked. She pointed at the brown, grey and white bird that had landed on a branch.

'I think it's a seagull,' I replied.

'But the sea is far from here!'

'Maybe it's lost.'

We called mum, dad and Kevin to come and see the bird. Soon, all five of us were in the garden watching the bird. It didn't seem to be afraid. It just stood on the lawn cleaning its feathers with its beak.

'It is a seagull,' said mum. 'But it's a young one and that's why the feathers are still a mixture of colours. When it grows up, it will be black and white.'
'What's it doing here?' asked my sister.
'Perhaps it was flying to some place and was lost.'
'What shall we do with it?' I asked.

Dad thought for a moment and then he said, 'Let's keep it here for a few days and feed it. Then we will see if it's strong enough to fly away back to where it belongs.'

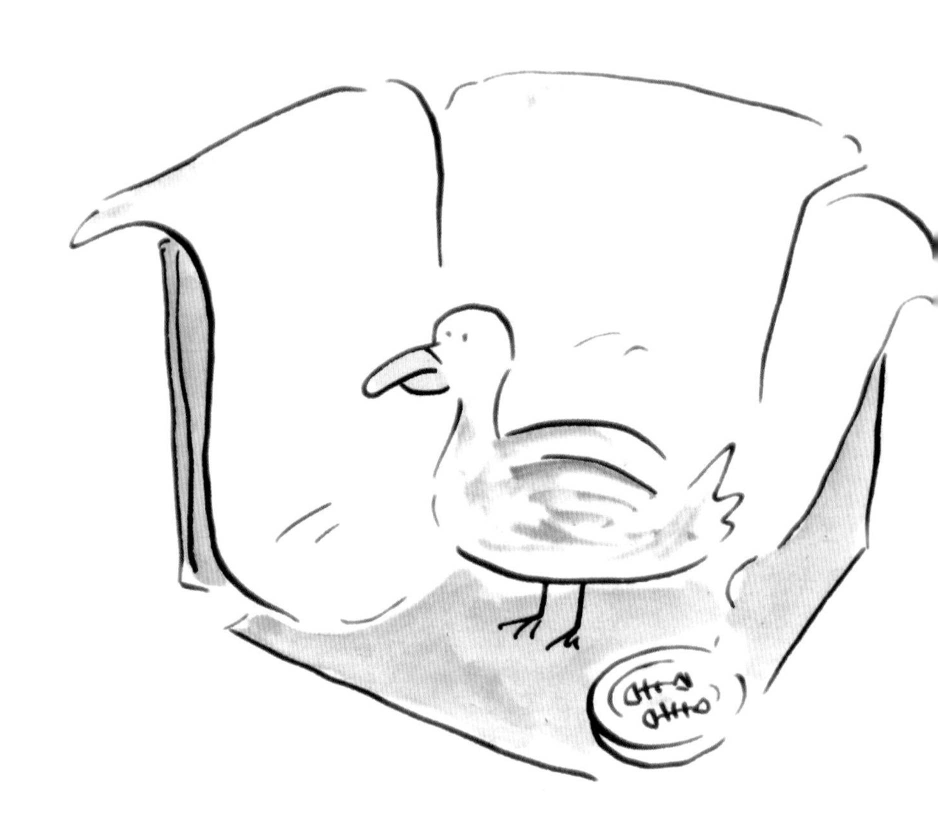

That afternoon we placed some old towels in a cardboard box so that the seagull would have a soft place to sleep. We opened a tin of sardines for its meal. The seagull wasn't scared of us at all! In fact, it seemed happy to be looked after. We named him 'Gull'.

'Seagulls like water, don't they?' asked Selina the next day. 'Maybe our seagull is missing the ocean. We need to make a pool for it to swim.'
'Good idea. But we don't have a pool or a bowl big enough.'
My sister thought for a moment. 'I know!' she said. 'What about the bathtub?'

We ran inside and filled the bathtub with cold water. When it was full, mum carefully placed Gull into the bathtub. We stepped back to see what would happen.

Gull paddled around for a moment and then started to dive into the water every now and then. Round and round the bathtub he went, splashing us and the bathroom floor. He liked it!

Another day, I sat in the garden and watched Gull play in the lawn. I thought that it would be great if we could teach him to fly around the neighbourhood and pick things with his beak and bring them back to us. Maybe, he could fly to the shop and bring back a bag of sweets. I could tie the money to one of his legs!

Or maybe, I could teach him to drop things on to my friends for fun. He would swoop low over them and drop biscuits!

The next day, dad called us together. ‘It is time that Gull should continue on his way,’ he said. ‘He is stronger now and he really should be back with the other seagulls.’
We all felt sad to think that we would be losing Gull. But dad was right. A seagull should be by the sea. Gull needed to be back with his family and friends.

We put Gull into a cardboard box and carried him to the beach.
When we got to the beach, we walked down the sand to the water and let Gull out of the box. He shook his feathers, looked at us and then took off into the air. He flew around us once and then flew out to sea, to some rocks in the distance.
We waved goodbye to Gull. That night I went to bed early and thought about Gull for a long time before falling asleep.

I woke up in the morning and I could hear my sister calling me. 'Come here, quick! You must see this!'
I jumped out of bed and ran outside in my pyjamas.
'Look! Up there on the roof!' shouted Selina.
I looked, and there, right on top of the roof was Gull! He gave a call, spread his wings and then flew once around my sister and me before heading up into the sky.
'Looks like he has two homes now,' said mum.
We were all happy.

Jamuna

Jamuna stretched out her trunk and reached for the apple that her keeper held. It was early morning at the zoo, Jamuna's favourite time. It was still quiet and there were no visitors yet. The cool air reminded Jamuna of growing up in the coolness of the jungle.

Jamuna had lived in the jungle with her mother, brothers and sisters and her cousins. Then one day humans came to their jungle and captured her and two other elephants. They had been loaded onto trucks and driven into a city and then to a harbour. There, Jamuna was separated from the other elephants. She was sent by ship to a country far, far away from India.

Her keepers at her new home were kind to Jamuna, and she was well looked after. There was always enough food and a dry place to sleep. There were older elephants at the zoo when Jamuna arrived. But now she was the old-est.

Jamuna often thought of her early days in the jungle. The days were full of wanderings among the green trees and eating fresh green leaves. Jamuna also remembered how they used to rest in the lake water during the hot months.

When Jamuna came to the zoo, children would take rides on her, they would sit in a chair strapped to her broad back. Around and around the pathway Jamuna would walk with the children swaying from side to side in the chair.

After many years, the weight of carrying the children on her back gave Jamuna pain in her knees and her feet. She had enjoyed hearing the children's laughter as they held on to the chair high above the ground. But Jamuna was happy when the rides came to an end.

Jamuna had always enjoyed playing tricks. She would have a bit of fun with her keepers or even with the visitors at the zoo. She would use her trunk to pluck at their sleeves or perhaps take their hats from their heads.

One day, Jamuna was a little more mischievous than usual and had escaped from her keeper. She tried to hide from him for a little while but was found out. On another occasion, she had fun in turning on all the water taps and then running away.

Jamuna was often used by the keepers to help with heavy jobs around the zoo. She was very strong and could lift, pull and push objects.

When Jamuna did such heavy jobs, she enjoyed the attention she got from the people who would crowd around to watch her.

Once, it rained very hard for several days. The stream running through the hippo pool had risen so much that the hippos were able to float over the barrier. They were wandering free around the zoo.

Jamuna and the other elephants helped to bring the hippos back into their area. Jamuna didn't speak the hippos' language but when she looked into their eyes they understood exactly what she wanted them to do. They went back into their pool.

‘Okay, Jamuna?’ her keeper asked. The keeper spoke into Jamuna’s ear. Jamuna was content and she swung her trunk back and forth while leaning against the keeper. Together they continued their walk along the quiet paths.

New words

barrier
bathroom
content
continue
coolness
distance
feather
harbour
hippo
holiday
mischievous
neighbourhood
paddle
pathway
pyjama
remember
remind
sardine
seagull
stay
weight

What did you learn?

The seagull that came to stay

What was the colour of the seagull?

What did the family give the seagull for its first meal?

In what did the seagull swim?

Jamuna

Where was Jamuna born?

What was the elephant's trick with taps?

How did the hippos escape from their pool?